Professor
THE EXECUTIONER'S BLOCK

by
David Webb

Illustrated by Derry Dillon
Did You Know? pages illustrated by
Helen Lake and Peter Hancock

First Published
October 09 in Great Britain by

PUBLISHING

ISBN-10: 1-905637-82-9
ISBN-13: 978-1-905637-82-9

Typeset by Educational Printing Services Limited

Educational Printing Services Limited

E-mail: enquiries@eprint.co.uk   Website: www.eprint.co.uk

Contents

Nutter Hall

Professor Nutter's battered green jeep pulled up abruptly on the wide gravel path at the front of a large, rambling black and white building.

'Well, Nigel, here it is!' said the Professor, proudly. 'Nutter Hall! What do you think of it?'

'It looks very old,' replied Nigel, staring

out of his window, 'and it's a bit . . . sort of
. . . crooked. Are you sure it's safe to stay
here, Uncle?'

'Of course it's old, you stupid boy – and
it's perfectly safe! It's a Tudor mansion. It
was built more than four hundred years ago!
I bet today's houses won't last that long!'

'I'm glad we're only staying for one
night,' muttered Nigel. 'It doesn't look very
comfortable.'

'Don't be so soft, boy!' snapped the Professor. 'It will be a marvellous experience – and it will help you with your school project. Now get your bag out of the back of the jeep and we'll go and find our room.'

Six stone steps led up to an impressive oak door and the Professor led the way proudly as they entered Nutter Hall.

As the name suggested, the building had once belonged to the Nutter family and the Professor couldn't wait to show off the grand old home of his ancestors. These days it was owned by a rich business man who had made his money in the nearby City of London. He had opened the Hall to the public, who were more than happy to pay to see such a fine example of a Tudor mansion.

Once inside, Nigel noticed a musty smell and, despite the fact that it was partly disguised by furniture polish, it made his nose twitch uncomfortably.

An elderly gentleman with a crown of snow white hair was sitting behind an equally elderly dark wooden desk in the entrance area and his face broke into a wrinkled smile when he saw the Professor.

'Good afternoon, Professor Nutter. How wonderful to see you again! And this must be your little nephew, Nigel?'

Nigel didn't like being called 'little' and he scowled and peered over his glasses at the man.

'Thank you, Thomas,' replied the Professor. 'It's good to see you again, too.

I hope you're keeping well.'

'I musn't complain,' said Thomas, rising slowly to his feet. 'A few aches and pains here and there but I'm eighty-four years old, you know!'

Nigel scowled again. Why did old people always insist on telling everyone their age?

'Marvellous! Marvellous!' gushed the Professor. 'Eighty-four years old! What do you think of that, Nigel?'

Nigel stared blankly at his uncle and made no reply.

'Well,' continued the Professor, 'perhaps you could show us up to our room, Thomas, so that we can get settled in?'

'It will be a pleasure,' replied Thomas, still beaming. 'Follow me.'

Thomas moved very slowly. Nigel and the Professor followed him as he shuffled through the entrance area and along a narrow passageway that led to the bottom of a winding staircase.

'You've been given the master bedroom,' said Thomas, beginning to climb the stairs. 'Obviously, it will be closed to visitors during your stay.'

'We're very honoured,' explained the Professor, then turning to Nigel he added: 'Only Nutters are allowed to stay overnight in Nutter Hall these days.'

Nigel stared at his uncle but didn't bother to reply.

At the top of the staircase, another dark, narrow passageway led to the master bedroom. Thomas pushed open the creaking door and stood to one side so that the Professor and Nigel could enter.

'I'll leave you to settle in,' he said, backing away. 'The camp bed is for Nigel. We thought it only right that you should have the four-poster, Professor. I'm sure the three of you will be very comfortable.

'Yes, I'm certain Sir William will be very pleased to see you again, Professor!'

Did You Know?

☐ The Tudor period lasted for 118 years from 1485 to 1603. The most famous of the Tudor monarchs is Henry VIII.

☐ There were six Tudor Kings and Queens – although Lady Jane Grey was never actually crowned! The Tudor monarchs are:

Elizabeth I

Henry VII
(1485 – 1509)
Henry VIII
(1509 – 1547)
Edward VI
(1547 – 1553)

Henry VIII

Jane Grey (1553 for 9 days)
Mary (1553 – 1558)
Elizabeth I (1558 – 1603)

▢ During the Wars of the Roses, the symbol of the Lancastrians had been a red rose and the symbol of the Yorkists had been a white rose. When Henry VII became the first Tudor King, the two symbols were combined together to form the Tudor rose.

▢ Queen Elizabeth I, the daughter of Henry VIII, was the longest reigning Tudor monarch. She was Queen from 17th November 1558 to 24th March 1603. She was also the last of the Tudors to reign.

▢ Lady Jane Grey was the shortest reigning of the Tudor monarchs at the tender age of fifteen – although she was never actually crowned. She was Queen for just nine days before being imprisoned in the Tower of London and eventually executed at the command of her Catholic cousin Mary Tudor.

The Picture

'What did he mean the three of us?' asked Nigel. He was standing in the doorway scratching his head. 'You didn't tell me anyone else was staying with us. And who on earth is Sir William?'

'Let me introduce you,' said the Professor with a wicked grin. 'Lead on into the room, Nigel. There's someone I'd like you to meet.'

Glancing suspiciously at his uncle, Nigel edged hesitantly through the open door and stared around the master bedroom. He was opening and closing his mouth like a goldfish.

A huge four-poster bed dominated the room. It jutted out from the back wall and directly in front of it was a large, leaded window which overlooked the front drive. An old wooden table was placed to one side of the bed and on top of it was a large blue patterned jug and matching bowl. To the other side of the four-poster was a tiny folding bed, which Nigel guessed was to be his resting place. It looked most uncomfortable.

Set into the wall, to the right of the four-poster bed, was a large open fireplace, the coals were kept in place by a blackened grill. The only other piece of furniture in the room was a wooden rocking chair, which had been placed so that anyone sitting in it could see out of the window.

Nigel took all this in within seconds and then, with a loud sniff, he turned towards the Professor and said: 'I don't understand, Uncle – who do you want me to meet?'

Still grinning, the Professor nodded towards the fireplace and replied: 'He's over there, Nigel. I think you might recognise him!'

Nigel stared across the room and his gaze fixed on the wall above the fireplace. His eyes widened and his mouth dropped open in astonishment. There, on the chimney breast above the fireplace, was a huge picture in a gilded frame. There was no mistaking the familiar face that stared down at Nigel; the same high forehead and wide, staring eyes; the same drooping moustache and pointed chin; even the same reddish-brown hair – just a lot more of it! There was no mistake – it was a picture of his uncle, the Professor.

'You're on the wall,' said Nigel, pointing towards the picture. 'What are you doing on the wall, Uncle?'

'Ah, that's where you are wrong,' said the Professor, taking a step forward. 'He may look like me, Nigel, but that is a picture of my ancestor Sir William Nutter. If you look closely you will see that he is wearing a golden pendant around his neck made up of two crossed swords on a shield. That is the Nutter Coat of Arms, Nigel. Also, if you look when the picture is dated you will see that it can't possibly be me.'

Sir William Nutter
1502 - 1533

Nigel moved closer. He stared at the golden pendant and then peered down at the small, brass plate screwed into the frame at the bottom of the painting. Sure enough the information was there for him to see clearly:

Sir William Nutter
1502 - 1533

'It's incredible!' muttered Nigel. 'If it wasn't for that silly hair and the funny clothes it could be you, Uncle!'

'Sir William Nutter,' repeated the Professor, staring proudly at the picture. 'He had quite a life – although I'm afraid it came to an abrupt end. He was a loyal supporter of King Henry VIII himself. Henry trusted him and asked his advice, but when Sir William opposed the King's marriage, Henry had him arrested for treason. He was taken from this very house in the middle of the night in October 1533, Nigel; dragged away beneath the full moon by Henry's soldiers.'

The Professor lowered his voice. 'It's said that his ghost returns to Nutter Hall each full moon.'

Nigel felt a cold shiver run down his spine. 'I – I don't believe in ghosts,' he muttered, his voice no more than a whisper. 'What happened to him when he was dragged away?'

'Two days later, he was led to the executioner's block,' continued the Professor. 'A huge crowd had gathered to witness his final moments. William's wife, Alice, and his young son Edward were present along with the maids and servants from Nutter Hall, desperately hoping for a last minute reprieve – but it wasn't to be. William knelt down and the hooded executioner raised his axe . . .'

'Don't tell me any more!' spluttered Nigel. 'I'll have nightmares, especially with that picture staring down at me!'

'Don't be so soft, boy!' hissed the Professor. 'It all happened hundreds of years ago! Times have changed a bit since then, you know!'

'Even so,' whimpered Nigel, 'I get upset very easily. You know I get upset, Uncle!'

The Professor shook his head in despair. 'It's a good job you weren't alive in Tudor times, boy. You wouldn't have lasted more than five minutes! Get your bag unpacked and we'll go and get something to eat.'

Did You Know?

▢ Tudor houses are
very distinctive
and there are still
many fine examples
standing today.
They are easily

recognised by their black and white
effect. Tudor houses were built by
constructing a strong timber frame and
then filling the wall spaces with **wattle
and daub**.

▢ **Wattle and daub** was made by weaving
sticks to form a tight panel. This was
called a wattle and it was fitted between
the timber beams and covered with daub, a
thick mixture of mud, sand, plant fibres
and animal dung! The wattle and daub was
usually whitewashed to brighten it up.

☐ If you look at a Tudor house it may appear
to be crooked or uneven. This is because
the wooden beams were cut by hand.
There were no machines in Tudor times to
make straight, regular beams.

☐ Tudor houses were built with a steeply
pitched roof which was usually covered
with tiles. The upper floor of a Tudor
house was often bigger than the ground
floor and would overhang.

☐ In the towns, the streets were narrow,
noisy – and very smelly and dirty! The
overhanging houses also meant that the
streets were dark and at night, there was
always the danger of being attacked and
robbed.

The Full Moon

'Are we eating in the Great Hall?' asked
Nigel, as they made their way back down the
narrow stairway towards the entrance area.
'That's where Sir William and his family and
his guests would have eaten back in Tudor
times. My history teacher, Mrs Biggins, has
told us all about Tudor mansions.'

'No, I'm afraid we're not,' replied the
Professor. 'Even though we're both Nutters,

we're not allowed to dine in the Great Hall. There are too many priceless items on display. Thomas's wife will have prepared supper in the kitchen, I'm afraid – where the servants used to eat.'

Thomas's wife was a small, grey haired woman who looked even older than Thomas. She was waiting for them in the kitchen, standing beside a huge, white oven, stirring a thick stew with a long wooden spoon. She forced a smile as Nigel and the Professor entered but there were gaps in her brown and broken teeth, so her smile looked more like a grimace.

'Nice to see you again Professor, it's been so long!'

Each time she pronounced the letter 's' a spray of spit shot out from her cracked teeth.

'It's good to see you, too, Annie,' said the Professor. 'You're looking well.'

'Not too bad, thank you, Sir. I'm eighty-five, you know!'

Nigel clenched his fists and frowned.

'This is my nephew, Nigel,' said the Professor, placing a hand on Nigel's shoulder. 'He's never been to Nutter Hall before.'

'You're so welcome, young Sir. You look just like your uncle.' She wiped her mouth with her sleeve and turning to the Professor, she said: 'Stew for supper, if that suits you?'

'That will be wonderful,' replied the Professor, as Nigel wondered how much spit had landed in the stew pot.

They sat at a bare wooden table that was as old and cracked as Annie's teeth. There were no windows in the room, just a small door that led into a back courtyard.

Moving slowly and carefully, Annie carried over the pot of steaming stew and served it with a ladle into two large bowls. It had a strange, pungent smell that seemed to fill the whole kitchen.

'I know the Professor likes my Tudor

stew,' hissed Annie. 'The recipe's an old favourite from Tudor times.'

Nigel frowned and stared into the bowl of steaming grey stew. It was mostly vegetables with a few pieces of pale meat floating near the greasy surface, as if they were trying to escape.

'It looks lovely,' lied the Professor, 'I've been looking forward to your Tudor stew all day, Annie.'

Nigel was lost for words.

Annie shuffled away and the Professor tucked in to his supper. 'Come on, lad, get it down. You'll get nothing else until breakfast.'

Reluctantly, Nigel picked up his spoon

and, taking a deep breath, he dipped it into his bowl. He pushed aside a piece of grizzly meat and scooped up some vegetables. It tasted awful but he was hungry – and it was a very long time until breakfast.

* * * * *

Back in the bedroom, Nigel was feeling sick. He was sitting on the end of the four-poster bed holding his stomach and groaning.

'I've got a delicate stomach,' he moaned. 'It's not used to Tudor stew!'

'You've been spoiled,' snapped the Professor, sharply. 'How do you think boys of your age survived back in Tudor times? They ate up all their stew, that's how!'

Nigel was about to point out that lots of boys his age didn't survive in Tudor times but he thought better of it. Instead, he staggered across to the window and unfastened the latch. He leaned out and took in a gulp of fresh air. It was then that he noticed the full moon. There it was, a huge, pale yellow disc rising in the night sky.

Nigel's heart missed a beat and his hands began to tremble. He let out a gasp and leapt back from the window, his lips quivering.

'Whatever's the matter with you, lad?' asked the Professor. 'You look as if you've seen a ghost!'

Ever so slowly, Nigel raised his arm and pointed through the open window towards the night sky.

'It's . . . it's . . . a full moon!' he stammered. 'We're staying the night at Nutter Hall and it's a full moon!'

'So it is,' said the Professor, joining his nephew at the open window. 'Well, well, well! We could be in for an interesting night, Nigel! A full moon and we're sleeping in Sir William Nutter's bedroom!'

Did You Know?

☐ Unlike today, much of the food eaten by
the Tudors was seasonal. Fruit, for
example, had to be eaten soon after it was
picked, although wealthy families might be
able to buy oranges and lemons imported
from Spain.

☐ Keeping food fresh was a real problem.
There were no fridges or freezers in
Tudor times, so food had to be stored in a
larder, which was kept as cool as possible.
Water came from pumps or wells. In
country areas, water was collected from
the local stream, which was often polluted
with sewage from a nearby town!

☐ The kitchens at Hampton Court were the
largest kitchens in Tudor England. Built to

feed the court of Henry VIII, they had to provide meals for up to 600 people twice a day. About 200 workers toiled in the noisy, hot kitchens to provide an endless supply of food.

☐ Rich people ate huge meals and often held banquets where they were served with different meats as well as seasonal fruit and vegetables, fish and bread. Poor people had to make do with a much simpler diet, such as soup or thin stew, bread, cheese and just the occasional piece of meat. The poor, including children, drank weak ale with their meal while the rich drank wine as well as ale.

The Priest Hole

Nigel woke up shivering. He didn't know
how long he had been asleep but something
had disturbed him and now he was shivering
with cold. There was a noise, a really strange
noise that seemed to be coming from
somewhere inside the bedroom and Nigel
realised that it was his uncle, snoring. In
fact, he was not so much snoring as snorting,
like some sort of animal in distress.

Nigel still felt ill. The stew was lying heavy in his stomach and as he sat up in bed he felt it swilling around. The window had been left open and the curtains had been drawn back so that the full moon cast an eerie yellow glow into the bedroom. It was just as well as there was no electric light in the room, just a candle and a box of matches which had been left on the small bedside table next to the four-poster.

The Professor snorted again, turned over in his bed and then snorted even louder.

'It's hopeless,' muttered Nigel to himself, 'I'll never get back to sleep.'

Nigel pushed the covers to one side and then climbed out of bed. He moved across to the window and stared out into the moonlit night. Everywhere was still and peaceful. An owl hooted in the distant woods and a black cat skulked slowly across the gravel driveway. Nigel shivered again and turned away from the window.

It was then that his gaze fell upon the picture. Sir William Nutter seemed to be gazing down on him from the wooden panel above the fireplace, his face eerily lit by the moonlight.

Putting his glasses on, Nigel moved forward, drawn toward the picture as if in a trance. Slowly and deliberately, Nigel reached out a trembling hand and touched the brass plate beneath the picture. Almost instantly, there was a clicking sound, as if a catch had been released and, to Nigel's astonishment, one of the small wooden panels to the left of the fireplace had opened ever so slightly, like a door left ajar. Nigel pushed the panel gently to reveal a dark space that seemed to stretch backwards behind the fireplace.

'It's a priest hole,' he said to himself. 'I've found a priest hole.'

Nigel stepped back and stared, his mouth wide open. He had discovered a secret room and he shivered with excitement. He peered again into the dark opening and wondered what to do next. A particularly loud snort reminded him that he was not alone in the room and he knew that he would have to tell his uncle.

Nigel rushed over to the four-poster bed and tugged at the covers. 'Uncle! Uncle! Wake up! I think I've found a priest hole!'

The Professor snuffled and grunted and pulled the covers over his head.

'Do wake up!' persisted Nigel, prodding his uncle in the back. 'I'm sure I've found a priest hole!'

The Professor stuck his head out of the covers and his eyes flickered open.

Priest hole? What are you talking about, boy?'

'Over here,' urged Nigel, indicating towards the fireplace. 'There's a secret panel and an opening and . . . I don't know what's behind it.'

The Professor reached for his glasses and then climbed out of bed. He was wearing a long nightgown and untidy wisps of hair stuck up from his head.

'Secret panel,' he repeated, moving towards the fireplace. 'It's possible, it's possible . . . there was always a rumour . . .'

'Look!' said Nigel, pointing to the left of the fireplace. 'It opened up when I touched the brass plate beneath the picture.'

'Well, I never,' said the Professor, slowly. 'It could be a priest hole, Nigel, although priest holes were used mostly in Queen Elizabeth's time, years after Sir William Nutter was executed.'

'I don't understand,' said Nigel. 'If it's not a priest hole, Uncle, What on earth is it?'

'Well, Nigel,' replied the Professor, scratching his head, 'I guess there's only one way to find out.'

Did You Know?

⬜ If you lived in Tudor times, your bedroom would be nowhere near as comfortable as a modern day bedroom. Even in wealthy homes, the Tudor bedroom would be freezing cold, especially in winter! There was, of course, no central heating! Rich people had the luxury of an open fireplace in their bedrooms but, even so, they would often wake up to find frost on the inside of their windows.

⬜ The master bedroom was usually dominated by an impressive four-poster bed. The 'roof' of the  bed meant that the sleepers were protected from bugs that often fell from the bedroom ceiling and curtains would be drawn around the bed to help keep out draughts.

☐ There would be little furniture in the bedroom – perhaps a chair near the window and a table with a jug and bowl for washing. There might also be a square rug laid on the wooden floorboards. Wealthy families would often hang pictures or portraits on the walls.

☐ It was during Tudor times that glass was first used in windows. Most windows were casement windows made up of small panes of glass held in place by lead. Casement windows could be opened outwards to let in fresh air. Poorer people could not afford glass windows and had to cover the gaps with cloth or even paper.

Through the Secret Passage

'I'm not going in there,' protested Nigel. 'It's dark and it's scary – and there might be spiders. You know I don't like spiders, Uncle.'

The Professor looked at his nephew in disbelief. 'Your great ancestor Sir William Nutter had his head chopped off and you're worried about a few little spiders? You should be ashamed of yourself, Nigel Nutter!'

'Well, perhaps I'll give it a try if you go first,' said Nigel reluctantly.

'Pass me the candle holder and the matches, Nigel – and get your slippers on. This is going to be really interesting. Who knows what we might find!'

The Professor lit the candle and made sure it was secured in its metal holder. Kneeling down on one knee, he peered through the open panel into the dark space beyond.

'It's not as small as I thought it would be.' The Professor's voice was no more than a whisper. 'It's quite deep; too deep to be just a priest hole. It seems to go back behind the fireplace.'

'Perhaps we should wait until morning?' suggested Nigel. 'It's been there for hundreds of years so a few more hours won't make any difference, will they?'

'Nonsense!' snapped the Professor. 'Where's your sense of adventure, lad? I'm going in. You keep close behind me.'

Slowly and cautiously, the Professor crept forward on all fours until he was in the gap behind the wooden panel. Nigel followed, his heart pounding and his bottom lip quivering with fear.

'What can you see?' he asked. 'Is there anything there?'

The only thing Nigel could see was the Professor's bottom.

'It's more like a tunnel or a passage,' replied the Professor. 'It's quite low but I think we'll just about be able to stand up. Make sure we keep together.'

The Professor pulled himself up into a standing position but the roof of the passage was so low that he was bent and stooped. He edged forward slowly, thrusting the flickering candle in front of him. It seemed to be getting colder and colder the deeper they moved into the secret passage.

Suddenly, the Professor stopped and Nigel bumped into the back of him.

'Why have we stopped?' he asked. 'Have we come to the end of the passageway?'

'Not the end of the passage,' explained the Professor. 'There are some steps going downwards. Be careful you don't stumble, Nigel.'

The Professor moved forward again, taking each step slowly and carefully. Down they went, one step at a time, nine in all and then the Professor stopped again and let out a gasp of disappointment.

'What's the matter?' asked Nigel, trying to peer over his uncle's shoulder. 'Is there a problem?'

'We've come to the end of the passageway,' said the Professor holding up the candle. 'There's just a wooden panel like in the bedroom.'

'Oh well – that's it,' said Nigel, in relief. 'Let's go back, should we?'

'Wait a minute,' whispered the Professor, 'there must be a way through.'

He prodded and pushed at the dark wooden panel but it would not give way. He scratched his head and pulled at his moustache and then he knelt down to examine the bottom of the panel.

'Aha!' he said. 'I think I've got it! Hold this, Nigel.'

The Professor passed the candle back to his nephew and pushed his fingers beneath the bottom edge of the panel. Ever so slowly, he eased the panel upwards until there was a gap big enough for them to crawl through.

'This is amazing!' gasped the Professor, standing upright. 'Surely there won't be any more surprises?'

'I do hope not,' whimpered Nigel. 'I do hope not!'

Did You Know?

◻ When Henry VIII became king in 1509,
England was a Catholic country and was
controlled by the Pope in Rome. The Pope
would not let Henry divorce his first wife,
Catherine of Aragon and so Henry made
himself head of the Church of England and
gave himself a divorce!

◻ Henry married his second wife, Anne
Boleyn, in 1533, hoping that she would
provide him with a son and heir to the
throne. However, she gave birth to a

daughter, Elizabeth. In January 1536, Anne did give birth to a son but sadly the child was born dead. Later that same year, Henry accused Anne of adultery (being unfaithful to him). Anne was imprisoned in the Tower of London before being beheaded on May 19th, 1536.

☐ When Henry VIII broke away from the Pope and the Catholic Church of Rome, he began to close down and destroy the monasteries. Monastery land was taken and sold off cheaply. Between 1536 and 1540, over 850 monasteries were either closed or destroyed.

Bolton Priory

☐ Henry was furious that monks and nuns continued to be loyal to the Pope and the Catholic Church. He began arresting monks for treason and they were sent to the executioner's block.

☐ Priest holes were secret hiding places built into many of the Catholic houses of England during Tudor times, when Catholics were persecuted. Most priest holes appeared during the reign of Queen Elizabeth I (Henry VIII's daughter) but the first priest holes were definitely earlier. Most priest holes were small and cramped but some led to a secret passage which was a means of escape when the soldiers arrived.

Portal to the Past

Nigel also crawled through the gap in the wall and stared around in the flickering candle light.

'Where are we?' asked Nigel. His hands were trembling again. 'I recognise this room; at least I think I do.'

'We're in the kitchen,' replied the Professor. 'I'm sure we're back in the kitchen. But there's something not right, Nigel. It's not quite the same.'

It was difficult to see in the semi-darkness. The dying embers of a fire smouldered in the huge stone fireplace; the lingering smell of Tudor stew hung in the air, reminding Nigel that he still felt sick; the long, wooden table stretched across the middle of the kitchen; the uneven stone floor felt cold beneath their feet, even through their slippers.

The Professor's eyes widened and he glanced back at the long, wooden table. There was something strange about the table. It didn't look as marked; it didn't look as polished but, more worryingly – it didn't look as old.

The sound of approaching footsteps made Nigel and the Professor jump and then turn towards the open doorway. A few seconds later, a plump, red faced woman appeared carrying a tray loaded with a pile of plates and a large blue jug. The moment she saw the Professor and Nigel, she let out a gasp of shock and dropped the tray to the floor. There was a crash of crockery as the plates crashed and the jug splintered.

The Professor rushed to her aid immediately.

'I'm so sorry,' he said, stooping down to pick up the tray, 'we didn't mean to frighten you.'

The startled woman just stood and stared, her eyes darting from the Professor to Nigel and then back to the Professor. Eventually she said:

'How did you get here so quickly, Sir William? I've only just collected the tray from you. I don't understand?'

'Sir William?' said the Professor, looking puzzled. 'No, no, no – there's some mistake! I'm not . . .'

'And who's this fine young man?' interrupted the woman. 'I've not seen him before!'

'This is my nephew, Nigel,' began the Professor. 'We're staying . . .'

'But you mustn't stay,' said the woman, interrupting again. 'We were tipped off that the soldiers are on their way. Remember? It's important that you leave under cover of darkness, Sir William. Young James is getting the horses ready in the yard!'

Nigel couldn't say a word. He just stood there opening and closing his mouth like a goldfish.

With a sudden shock of realisation, the Professor stared at the gap in the bottom of the wall and then at the wooden table and then at the woman. 'What's your name?' he asked her, slowly.

'Why, my name's Sarah,' replied the woman, looking puzzled. 'You know my name's Sarah, Sir William.'

'He's not Sir William!' blurted out Nigel, suddenly finding his voice. 'He may look like Sir William but he's my uncle, the Professor!'

The very next moment there was a shout from the Great Hall, followed by a commotion of voices. A young boy about the same age as Nigel dashed into the kitchen.

'They're here!' he yelled, a look of panic on his face. 'The soldiers have come for Sir William!'

There were more yells and the sound of fists beating on the front door that led into the Great Hall. And then the strangest thing happened. A figure appeared in the open doorway leading into the kitchen. A figure that made the Professor's blood run cold; a figure that made Nigel gasp with amazement, for the figure looked exactly the same as his uncle!

Sir William Nutter stumbled into the kitchen and pointed at the startled Professor.

'Who are you?' he said. 'You're me! I mean, I'm you! Oh, for goodness sake – who's who?'

Did You Know?

☐ There was so much sickness and disease in Tudor times that nine out of ten people died before they were forty. Only the rich could afford a doctor and the doctors had little idea how to cure people.

☐ Many people died of **sweating sickness** in Tudor times. This awful disease began with a feeling of fear followed by violent shivering, dizziness and headaches. Soon after, a fever would break out, causing the victim to sweat. The final stage of the disease was when the exhausted victim felt the need to sleep. All of this could happen within twenty-four hours and most victims did not survive.

☐ One popular cure for illness was called 'blood letting'. This involved cutting a slit in the body to let out bad blood. The Tudors believed this was a cure for almost anything. Leeches (creatures like earthworms but with sharp teeth) were also used to suck out blood. No wonder so many Tudor patients fainted with shock!

☐ Toilet facilities were very basic in Tudor times. Toilets were often just a piece of wood placed over a hole in the ground. There would often be enough room for six people to go at the same time! However, King Henry VIII had his own private toilet, which had a padded seat made with ribbons and golden studs.

▢ People did not wash a great deal in Tudor times and baths were thought to be unhealthy. Rich people covered themselves with strong perfume while the poor just smelt awful!

▢ There were no toothbrushes in Tudor times and so people tried to clean their teeth with a toothpick and a piece of cloth. Sugar became popular, especially with the rich. The result was their teeth became black and rotten. By the end of her reign, Queen Elizabeth only had a few rotten, blackened teeth left in her mouth.

Soldiers in the Night

For a few confusing seconds, Sir
William Nutter and the Professor stood
facing each other across the dimly lit
kitchen as the soldiers battered at the
door.

It was Sarah who stirred them into
action.

'You must escape,' she urged, looking

from Sir William to the Professor and then back to Sir William again. 'The soldiers will break down the door any moment! They'll take you to the Tower!'

Sir William moved further into the kitchen and glanced around in panic.

'How can we escape?' he asked. 'The soldiers are upon us!'

'The back door!' yelled Sarah, pointing the way. 'James has the horses ready in the yard. You can escape through the woods. You must all follow James!'

The boy moved over to the wooden door and pulled it open ever so slightly. He peered through the gap and then closed the door immediately. He stood with his back against the door, his bottom lip quivering.

'It's too late,' he cried. 'They're waiting in the yard! I saw them!'

'The passage,' said Nigel, pointing to the gap in the wooden panelled wall. 'We can hide in the secret passage until they've gone.'

'Quick, there's no time to lose,' said Sarah, as the sound of splintering wood echoed from the Great Hall. 'You lead the way, Master.'

Sir William Nutter was through the gap in seconds. Nigel went next, scampering through on all fours like a frightened mouse escaping into its mouse hole. The Professor knelt down ready to follow but in his haste his glasses slipped off the end of his nose and fell to the floor.

'My glasses, my glasses,' he muttered, feeling for them with his hands. 'I can't see a thing without my glasses!'

The soldiers were in the building. They were shouting and yelling and charging through the Great Hall.

'My glasses,' repeated the Professor. 'Where are my glasses?'

James rushed forward to help the

Professor – but it was too late. The first of the soldiers burst into the kitchen and pointed at the frightened boy.

'Stay where you are!' he commanded, as several other soldiers joined him. 'All of you stay exactly where you are!'

Sarah, James and the Professor froze like statues as yet more burly soldiers crowded into the kitchen. Behind them, the wooden panel in the wall slid silently downwards, leaving only the smallest of gaps close to the cold stone floor.

The commander of the soldiers, a cruel looking man with a stubbly chin and piercing green eyes, took two steps forward, so that he was standing directly in front of the kneeling Professor. Suddenly, there was a crunch of glass as the soldier ground the Professor's glasses into the floor with his great, black boot. The other soldiers laughed and jeered.

'Sir William Nutter,' said the commander, and he pulled the Professor to his feet, 'I arrest you for treason against the King. Do you have anything to say for yourself?'

'Did you say . . . *treason?*' repeated the Professor. He was shaking like a leaf. 'There must be some mistake. I'm only here for the weekend!'

'You can't do that!' yelled James, rushing forward. 'Leave him alone, you great brute!'

The commander scowled and swung his arm at the boy, sending him sprawling backwards until he crashed against the long, wooden table.

'One more word from you,' snapped the commander, 'and you'll join your master in the Tower!'

'The Tower,' gulped the Professor. 'I don't like the sound of that!'

'Take him away,' ordered the commander, and two snarling soldiers stepped forward and grabbed the Professor by his arms.

A cruel grin crept across the commander's face as the Professor was dragged from the kitchen struggling and squirming.

'You can rest assured,' he said, turning to Sarah and James, 'the trial will be swift and the punishment will be final. The scaffold is already built and the executioner's block awaits!'

Did You Know?

▢ Tudor soldiers were armed with pikes and longbows. English soldiers were feared because of their skill with the longbow. They also carried swords and daggers for hand to hand fighting.

▢ There was a constant threat of invasion during Tudor times, either from the Spanish or the French. Henry VIII built up the English navy into a fearful fighting force. His ships were well equipped with the latest cast iron canons.

▢ The most famous ship in Tudor times was the Mary Rose. The ship was named after Henry VIII's sister Mary and the Tudor rose, which was the emblem of the Tudors. The crew of the Mary Rose consisted of

200 sailors, 185 soldiers and about 35 gunners. You can imagine that conditions on board ship were very cramped and uncomfortable! The Mary Rose capsized and sank during the Battle of the Solent in 1545.

▢ During the reign of Queen Elizabeth I, newly invented muskets were used against the Spanish Armada in 1558. A musket was a long gun which was fired from the shoulder. A few years later, the musket took over completely from the longbow.

The Road to London Town

Half an hour after the Professor had been dragged away to the Tower, four forlorn figures were sitting at the wooden table in the kitchen of Nutter Hall. Nigel was shocked and shaken and his face was deathly pale.

'I don't understand what you're doing here,' said Sir William. He was sipping warm ale from a large tankard. 'Who are you? Where have you come from?'

Nigel thought for a moment before replying.

'We're your ancestors,' he said, carefully considering his words. 'Or rather you are our ancestor. Anyway, it's a long story and, apart from the secret passage, I'm not really too sure how we got here.'

'Your uncle, the Professor,' continued Sir William, 'he looked so like me.'

'That's why they took him,' said Sarah. 'The soldiers have got the wrong prisoner. They think he's you, Sir William!'

'Wh-what will happen to him?' asked

Nigel, although in his heart he already knew the answer.

There was a moment's icy silence. It was young James who replied, his voice barely a whisper.

'You heard the commander's words – *the scaffold is built and the executioner's block awaits*. I'm afraid they will . . .'

'I can't let that happen!' interrupted Sir William. He slammed his tankard down on the wooden table so that the ale spilled out. 'I should never have spoken out about the King's marriage! I don't understand why anyone would want more than one wife, anyway!'

Nigel nodded his head, slowly. He

agreed with that statement – but he was beginning to understand the charge of treason against Sir William.

'It's not really another wife he wants, is it?' said Sarah. 'King Henry wants a son, an heir to the throne. If the new Queen can give him a son, if Anne can only give him a son . . .'

'Nevertheless,' snapped Sir William, rising to his feet, 'I will not see an innocent man face the executioner's block, especially if he's a Nutter, like me!'

'There's nothing you can do about it,' insisted Sarah. 'You have to accept that the Professor is doomed.'

'There must be a way,' said Sir William, and he banged his fist on the wooden table in frustration.

Sir William Nutter pushed his chair to one side and paced up and down the kitchen. He wrung his hands together, he muttered and grumbled to himself, he walked across to the back door and stared up at the full moon. Suddenly, he turned back towards the table and, raising one finger in the air he announced: 'I've got it! I know what I must do! Yes, I know exactly what I have to do!'

* * * * *

Professor Nutter, his wrists tightly

bound, was sitting on a huge, grey horse,
surrounded by the King's soldiers. The
journey was long and uncomfortable and,
unused to riding, the Professor was being
jolted and shaken like a bag of beans. He
was cold, too, his slippers and nightgown
offering little protection against the chilly
night air. Above him, in the starlit sky, the
full moon shone down, lighting the road to
London Town.

The Professor knew what fate awaited
him. It would take a miracle to save him
from the executioner's block – but, then
again, miracles could happen – couldn't they?

Did You Know?

▢ In Tudor times, London was the largest
  city in Western Europe and by far the
  biggest city in Britain. There were 75,000
  people living in London when Henry VII
  became king in 1485. By 1600 the
  population had risen dramatically to
  200,000.

▢ Tudor London was a busy, bustling city.
  Visitors complained about the crowded
  streets and the noise. They also
  complained about the smell of rotting
  rubbish and about the thieves and
  pickpockets who roamed the town.

▢ There was a lot of crime in Tudor London.
  Most criminals were poor people who had
  to steal to survive. There were no

policemen but punishment for those caught was cruel. Murderers and thieves were usually hung while traitors faced the executioner's block. For minor crimes, such as small thefts or cheating a customer, criminals were put in the stocks so that people could throw rotten food at them!

☐ The streets in London were narrow and crowded. One of the biggest problems was getting rid of litter and sewage. There were no flushing toilets so poorer homes had to use a bucket. Their waste was often thrown out from a top window, which was unfortunate for anyone walking in the street beneath!

⧠ A gutter or channel ran down the middle of most streets. However, it collected rubbish, waste food and even sewage. The smell was awful and the streets were plagued by rats. It was only a matter of time before the outbreak of a serious plague.

⧠ There were all kinds of different shops in Tudor London. There were butchers and bakers, tailors, candle makers and shoemakers.

The shopkeeper would use the lower room as a workshop. Each morning, the shutter of the downstairs window would be lowered to form a counter. The shopkeeper and his family would live in the upper room above the shop.

❑ London was the most important trading city in Tudor England. The River Thames was lined with ships. Wealthy merchants imported and exported goods to all corners of the globe. However, the river was filthy as sewage and waste was simply dumped into it, causing sickness and disease.

❑ London was a harsh city in which to live. Even minor crimes were severely punished. At one end of London Bridge, the rotting heads of those executed for treason would be displayed as a warning to others on the Bridge Gate.

The Executioner's Block

It was exactly one month since the soldiers had arrived in the night and taken the Professor prisoner. The trial had gone badly and, as expected, the prisoner was found guilty of treason. Now, as he waited in the dark Tower dungeon, the Professor had given up any hope of a pardon. He had been given a simple set of clothes in which to take his last walk; a long, loose brown shirt, some ill-fitting trousers and a pair of plain black shoes. The morning seemed to drag on forever but as the hours passed he could hear the noisy crowd gathering.

Time ticked away – and then he heard the key turn in the lock and the dungeon door swung slowly open.

* * * * *

Three hooded figures pushed their way through the excited crowd that lined the way from Traitors' Gate to Tower Hill. The afternoon sky was dark grey and a thin drizzle had begun to fall.

'We need to get nearer to the scaffold,' muttered Sir William Nutter. 'If we are to have any chance, we need to get nearer.'

They eased through the jostling crowd until they were within touching distance of the scaffold. Nigel had never felt so nervous in his life. He couldn't understand why so many people had gathered to view an execution. There were all sorts of people, men dressed in their finery, tradesmen, even women with young children, all present to witness the execution of the traitor, Sir William Nutter.

Nigel stared at the wooden scaffold. Even though it looked blurry to him – he'd hidden his glasses away to avoid drawing attention to himself - he shivered with sheer fright. Four wooden steps led up to the raised platform, which had been covered with straw. Two guards stood at the top on either side of the steps. They were as still as statues as they stared out at the crowd. In the very centre of the platform was the executioner's block and Nigel let out a gasp of shock as he noticed that there were deep cuts in the block and even a dark stain, showing that it was not the first time the block had been used for execution.

To the right of the block, standing absolutely still, was the executioner, his hood already in place so that Nigel could not see his face. He was a large man with broad shoulders and thick arms. He held his hands in front of him, resting on the top edge of his axe, the long wooden handle reaching down to the floor.

Above the scene, the clouds darkened even more. It looked as if a storm was gathering.

Suddenly, the crowd fell silent. A single, steady drum beat could be heard. It echoed eerily in the darkening afternoon.

'He's on his way,' whispered James. 'It won't be long now.'

'What if it goes wrong?' whimpered Nigel. 'What if our plan doesn't work?'

'Remember what I've asked you to do,' said Sir William, confidently. 'You do your job and leave the rest to me!' And then he removed a golden pendant from his neck – the same golden pendant that Nigel had seen on the picture in the bedroom – and pressed it into Nigel's hand. 'Here,' he said, quietly, 'I have no more use for this. Make sure you give it to your uncle.'

The crowd parted and the Professor came into view. He was walking slowly towards the wooden scaffold, led by grim faced guards. Members of the crowd jeered as he passed and one boy of about Nigel's age thrust forward a hand with a half eaten apple.

'D'you want a bite?' he said, sarcastically.

'Not much point, is there?' replied the Professor, calmly and he continued his slow journey to the scaffold.

Nigel's heart was beating much faster than the steady, dull beat of the drum and when he looked down at his hands he noticed that they were shaking uncontrollably.

The guards, with the Professor in the middle, walked past the three hooded figures. Nigel could almost reach out and touch his uncle. They climbed the four wooden steps and mounted the platform. Suddenly, the drum stopped and the crowd waited in expectation. The guards stood to one side and the Professor turned to face the people. He was thin and gaunt and the few wisps of white hair he had left had grown long and straggly.

A soldier mounted the steps and approached the Professor. Nigel recognised him; it was the commander who had burst into the kitchen and arrested the Professor.

'Sir William Nutter, you have been found guilty of treason and you face the executioner's block.' His voice boomed out into the gloomy afternoon. 'Do you have any final words for the good people of London?'

'You have made a mistake,' said the Professor, feebly. 'I have nothing more to say!'

'Then let the execution commence!' bellowed the commander.

'Two guards took hold of the Professor's arms and led him towards the block as the drum began to beat once more. The executioner picked up his axe and held it firmly with both hands. Nigel could not bear to look.

The drum stopped.

The air was tense.

In the distance there was a rumble of thunder.

The Professor knelt down and placed his head on the block.

The executioner raised his axe and it hung in mid-air for what seemed like an eternity.

Did You Know?

☐ The history of the Tower of London dates back to 1080, when William the Conqueror began to build a huge white stone tower at the centre of his London fortress.

☐ Although the White Tower was the original building, over the centuries several more buildings were added, set within defensive walls and surrounded by a moat.

☐ In Tudor times, the Tower of London was both a prison and a place of execution where more than 130 men and women were sent to the executioner's block to be beheaded. The crime was usually treason – being disloyal or plotting against the King or Queen.

⬜ There have always been ravens at the Tower of London. They are cared for by the Ravenmaster. At least six black ravens are free to go anywhere within the tower grounds. Legend says that the Tower of London and the kingdom will fall should the ravens ever leave.

⬜ Rumour has it that several ghosts haunt the Tower of London. There is even a tale that many years ago the ghost of a huge grizzly bear appeared within the grounds, scaring a guard so badly that he dropped dead of shock!

⬜ Lady Jane Grey, 'The Nine Day Queen', was executed on 12th February, 1554. It is claimed that her ghost appears as a white, shimmering figure every year on the anniversary of her execution.

The Gathering Storm

Sir William Nutter leapt forward onto the steps and was up on the wooden scaffold in a flash.

'STOP!' he bellowed, and his voice echoed over the heads of the stunned crowd. 'I beg you to STOP! The wrong man is on the executioner's block!'

At first a murmur passed through the

crowd and then it grew into a babble of confusion. The people wanted to see an execution. Who was this hooded figure who dared to spoil their entertainment? Even the guards looked shocked. They stood and watched in amazement as the hooded figure stood at the very front of the scaffold and faced the crowd.

'You have the wrong man!' he repeated and ever so slowly he removed his hood.

The crowd let out a gasp as the stranger revealed his face.

'I am Sir William Nutter of Nutter Hall!' he proclaimed. 'It is my head that should be on the block!'

Nigel and James moved quickly in the

chaos that followed. They darted forward and scrambled beneath the scaffold, crawling on all fours. Within seconds they were out at the back of the structure, near to where the Professor still knelt with his head on the block, too frightened to move.

Nigel crouched down on his hands and knees and James climbed onto his back, so that he could see onto the raised scaffold. It seemed that everyone had forgotten about the Professor. He had been left completely on his own as the guards and even the executioner moved forward to grab their new victim.

'Professor!' hissed James. 'Follow me! We must move quickly!'

The Professor twitched on the block but made no effort to rise.

'Professor Nutter, I urge you to act quickly! We must make our escape!'

This time the Professor reacted. Removing his head from the block, he crawled forward on his hands and knees towards the voice.

'Come on, Professor,' urged James, 'climb down from the scaffold.'

The Professor was so unsteady that he crawled forward again and fell off the edge of the platform, landing with a thump on the damp ground.

'Hello, Uncle,' said Nigel, as the Professor shook his head and tried to focus. 'I'm glad to see you managed to keep your head!'

* * * * *

The three escapees edged their way along the banks of the River Thames and then up into the woods, where James had left the horses tethered and waiting. The gathering storm was moving closer, the deep rumbles of thunder getting louder and the streaks of lightning lighting up the dark grey sky. Nigel handed his uncle the golden

pendant that Sir William had pressed into
his hand and the Professor slipped it over
his head without speaking.

He had hardly said a word and he was
so weak that James and Nigel had to help
him onto his horse.

Suddenly, there was a frightening flash
of silver lightning followed almost at once by
a deafening crash of thunder. As the
grumbling, rolling thunder finally faded,
there was another noise; a noise that sent a

chill down the spines of the three escapees. In the distance, the crowd in front of the scaffold was cheering. The Professor looked at Nigel, whose eyes were wide with fear and disbelief and then he looked at James and said:

'The people have been granted their wish. The executioner has done his job for this day.'

He had no sooner spoken than the dark clouds above him burst and the rain pelted down relentlessly.

Did You Know?

▢ There were various traditions observed at
executions. The scaffold, which was a
raised wooden platform, was covered with
straw. The prisoner was usually allowed to
address the crowd and was also expected
to pay the executioner to do a good, clean
job.

▢ Most of those who were executed were
beheaded in front of huge crowds on
Tower Hill. However, six prisoners,
including Anne Boleyn and Henry VIII's
fourth wife, Katherine Howard, were given
the privilege of a private execution on
Tower Green.

◻ Most executions were carried out using an axe but Anne Boleyn was beheaded by a skilled swordsman from France.

◻ The executioner, normally the public hangman, usually wore a black mask so that neither the crowd nor the victim could see his face.

◻ Each victim of the executioner was offered a blindfold before being led to the block. This was to prevent them from seeing the axe and moving their head at the last moment.

The Picture on the Wall

It was late when they arrived back at Nutter Hall. The storm had passed over and the full moon was shining once again from the clear sky. Sarah was waiting for them. She was pleased to see the Professor back safe and sound but there was no smile on her face when she realised that her master, Sir William Nutter, had not returned.

'I've got some supper ready for you,'

she said, showing them into the kitchen. A roaring log fire was burning in the great stone fireplace. It crackled and spat as they sat at the long, wooden table. 'I've made you some stew. I hope you like it.'

'My favourite,' muttered Nigel, and he tried not to pull a face.

James did not speak. It had been Sir William's favourite meal, too.

After supper, Nigel and the Professor found themselves alone in the kitchen. The candles had burned down and the only light was an eerie orange glow from the dying embers of the fire.

'We haven't got long,' said the Professor. 'We must get back before the full moon disappears.'

Nigel stared at his uncle and wondered if being locked up in the Tower had sent him a bit mad.

'Come on,' said the Professor, 'I think we'll make a move.'

He got up slowly and shuffled across the kitchen until he stood before the wooden panel that led into the secret tunnel.

'You'll have to help me,' continued the Professor. 'I still feel a bit weak. Besides, I haven't got my glasses.'

Nigel knew what was required. He put his own glasses back on and moved across to join the Professor. Then he knelt down and slipped his fingers beneath the wooden panel. The panel eased upwards and he stared into the dark space beyond.

'You go first this time,' said the Professor. 'You'll be able to find your way better than me.'

Without glancing back, Nigel squeezed through the opening into the darkness and the Professor followed. They crept forward slowly, feeling their way through the pitch black passage and then climbing the steps that led to the bedroom, finally leaving the past behind them.

* * * * *

Nigel opened his eyes and wondered where he was. He still had a strange feeling in his stomach and he remembered the

Tudor stew. He was tired, too, even though he had only just woken up. Nigel yawned and stretched and then glanced across to the four-poster bed. He was surprised to see that his uncle was already awake. The Professor, wearing his nightshirt, was sitting bolt upright staring across the room at the picture above the fireplace, a startled look on his pale face.

There was his ancestor Sir William Nutter staring back at him.

'It was a dream, wasn't it?' said Nigel, throwing off the covers. 'The Tudor stew probably upset my stomach. Tell me it was only a dream, Uncle?'

'I don't think it was a dream,' replied the Professor, reaching for his glasses. They were not on the bedside table where he had left them the night before.

Nigel clambered out of the small, uncomfortable bed, wandered across the room and stood in front of the picture on the wall. He reached out a hand and touched the brass plate beneath. Nothing happened. Something was bothering him. He stared hard at the picture of Sir William. There was something not right. And then he knew what was wrong and a cold shiver ran down his spine. The golden pendant was missing! The golden pendant showing the two crossed swords on the shield was not around Sir William Nutter's neck!

Nigel turned back to his uncle who was still sitting bolt upright in bed. In a sudden moment of realisation, the boy's eyes

widened and he let out a gasp of shock.
Nigel stared with his mouth open as the
Professor raised his hand ever so slowly and
placed it on the golden pendant that hung
proudly around his wrinkled neck.

Also available from

PUBLISHING

Professor Nutter series by David Webb

This series combines fiction and fact in an original way. Between each chapter is a 'Did You Know?' page, which adds interest and provides information for the young reader.

Professor Nutter and the Curse of the Pharaoh's Tomb
ISBN 978-1-905637-42-3

When Professor Nutter finds an old map hidden in a secret room, it is the start of an amazing adventure. The map appears to show the site of an undiscovered Pharaoh's tomb and so the Professor and his nephew Nigel travel to Egypt in search of the secret burial place. Will they fall victim to the Curse of the Pharaoh's Tomb?

Professor Nutter and the Gladiator's Ghost
ISBN 978-1-905637-59-1

When Professor Nutter and his nephew Nigel camp out on the moors, they are awoken in the night by ghostly sounds. Through the swirling mist they see a legion of Roman soldiers marching along the road. However, when they are confronted by the gladiator's ghost, it is the start of a journey back in time to the greatest theatre of all...

Grandma's Teeth by David Webb
ISBN 978-1-905637-20-1

Dudley Drummond's half term is ruined when his awful Grandma comes to stay. Things go from bad to worse when she loses not one but two sets of false teeth! The story moves at a fast pace, with a trip to the dentist, a disastrous bus journey and a run in with local vandals.

Dinosaur Day by Ian MacDonald
ISBN 978-1-904374-67-1

It's Dinosaur Day and Terri Timpson is really excited. However, her class trip to the dinosaur exhibition at the City Museum provides far more excitement than she bargained for! Cunning thieves plan to steal the priceless Stone of Methesda from the Egyptian Gallery - until Terri and her friends leap into action! An exciting and hilarious adventure, that will keep its readers gripped to the end.

Trevor's Trousers by David Webb
ISBN 978-1-904904-19-9

How can a pair of trousers cause so much trouble? When Trevor promises to look after his new school trousers, it proves an impossible task. A priceless ruby ring, blundering thieves and a trip to the town tip can only lead to disaster! Poor Trevor! At least there is a reward waiting for him at the end of the adventure...

Friday the Thirteenth by David Webb
ISBN 978-1-905637-37-9

On Friday the thirteenth, Callum has to walk to school in the freezing cold, as he's been held up by his annoying sister. Things go from bad to worse when Callum arrives at school late to face Mr Wiggins, his strict teacher who makes him look after the dreadful Daisy, a new girl at school. However, Callum rises to the challenge when the school computers are stolen and Friday the thirteenth turns into his lucky day!

The Library Ghost by David Webb
ISBN 978-1-904374-66-4

It's Victorian Day at Mill Street School to help raise money for a new library! Children and staff are all dressed up in Victorian costume. All except for the sneering spoilsport, Delia Grime, that is. All goes well until Delia causes chaos at the coffee afternoon, trying to kidnap a valuable Victorian china doll. However, she's in for a ghostly shock when she makes her escape to the old school library!

Sam's Spitfire Summer by Ian MacDonald
ISBN 978-1-905637-43-0

When Sam is evacuated, he might as well be going to the moon.
Ten-year-old Sam watches the familiar sights of London
disappear in a cloud of steam as he sets off on a journey to the
unfamiliar world of country cottages, farmyard animals and a
hostile welcome at the village school.

Powder Monkey by Ian MacDonald
ISBN 978-1-905637-65-2

One minute Jack is zapping aliens on his keypad - the next, he's
fetching powder for the 32-pound guns on board HMS Victory.
Jack, a reluctant time traveller, is stuck in the middle of
preparations for one of the most famous sea battles ever
fought: Trafalgar. Jack learns about life aboard Nelson's
flagship the hard way; eating maggoty ship's biscuits, trying to
stay in a hammock and climbing to the mast head in a raging
storm. The tension mounts as the Victory advances on the enemy
fleet, and the dreadful realisation dawns on Jack...Nelson's ship
will be first to taste the French guns...

Alien Teeth by Ian MacDonald
ISBN 978-1-905637-32-4
Selected for the SLA Boys into Books (5-11) 2008 List.

When you accidentally sit on a set of teeth, they can be hard to
remove from your bottom...especially when they belong to an
alien who left them behind on a flying visit to Earth. The
precious molars belong to Emperor Zarg and he wants them
back!

On the Run by Stephanie Baudet
ISBN 978-1-905637-83-6
Tina's delighted to make friends with Peter during her family
holiday, however, her sister, is suspicious. She is convinced that
Peter is one of the boat joyriders who have been putting
people's lives at risk. Eventually Peter admits he has run away
from home to look for his father. While the two sisters are
helping him in his search, they discover the joyriders' plans to
commit a disastrous crime and try to stop them before it's too
late...

Jade Fry, Private Eye by Suzi Cresswell
ISBN 978-1-905637-75-1

Jade is fed up when she has to stay with her Gran. But life
there is more exciting than expected as she is soon swept up in
an exciting adventure involving Gran's pony, Captain. Captain is
important to Gran's friend, a race horse trainer whose star
horse, Smithy, is due to run in the Melton Chase soon. Without
Captain by his side Smithy won't get into the horse box. But it
seems that someone wants to stop him competing when Captain
disappears. Jade turns detective and follows the trail to find
out what is going on...

Cracking Up by Sandra Glover
ISBN 978-1-904904-86-1
Selected for the SLA Boys into Books (5-11) 2008 List.

With his mum in hospital and stressed at school thanks to his
awful teacher, Jamie thinks his life can't possibly get any worse.
Until he meets a lollipop lady who thinks she is a fairy
godmother. It's all nonsense – but why do wishes suddenly start
coming true, with disastrous consequences? Jamie attempts to
solve the mystery – but the solution is far more bizarre than
they could ever imagine.

The Bears Bite Back by Derek Keilty
ISBN 978-1-905637-36-2

This is a humorous and wacky sequel to Goldilocks and the Three
Bears. The bears are fuming after the ringleted prowler has
left their place in a mess. They quickly decide to get their own
back by following the intruder's footprints and marching over to
her house to eat her food, break her furniture and sleep in her
bed!

Magic Beans on Toast by Derek Keilty
ISBN 978-1-905637-58-4

Zoe plants a magic bean and is soon scaling an enormous
beanstalk to Giant land where she is captured by the grandsons
of the Giant from Jack and the Beanstalk...

Order online @ **www.eprint.co.uk**